Contents

*C = copper; B = bronze; S = silver; ( ) = the line must be played but cannot be assessed for a Medal.

Teacher on a Pogo Stick

Sally Adams

AB 3027

A Didgeridoodle

Colin Cowles

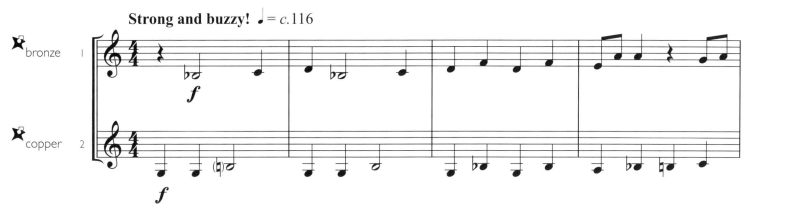

Gavotte

Dandrieu arr. Sally Adams

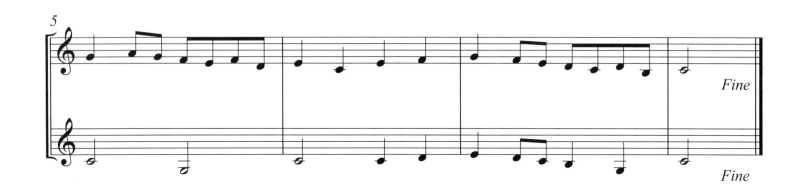

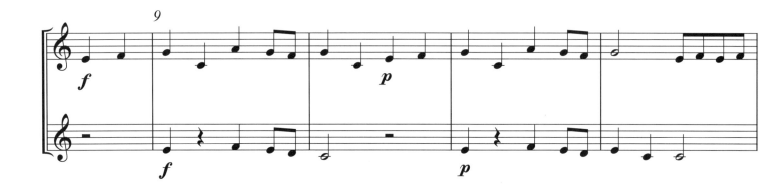

Humoresque

König arr. Sarah Watts

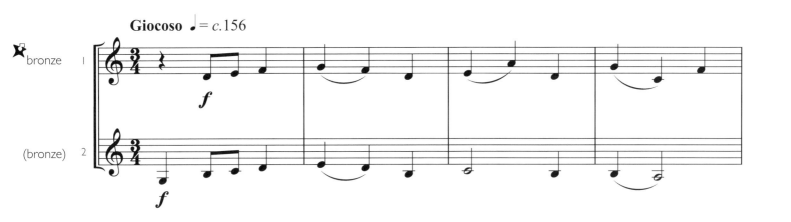

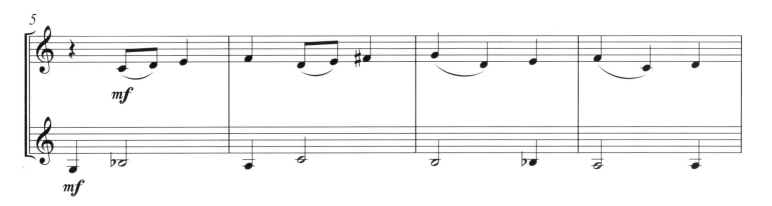

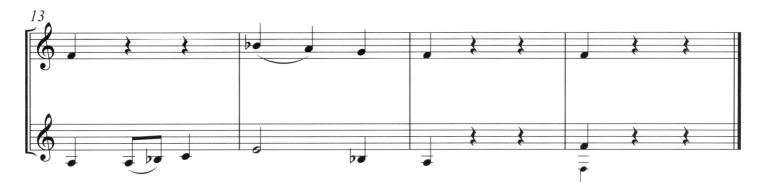

Sticky Toffee Tango

Paul Harris

AB 3027

Spring

from *The Four Seasons*

Vivaldi arr. Mark Goddard

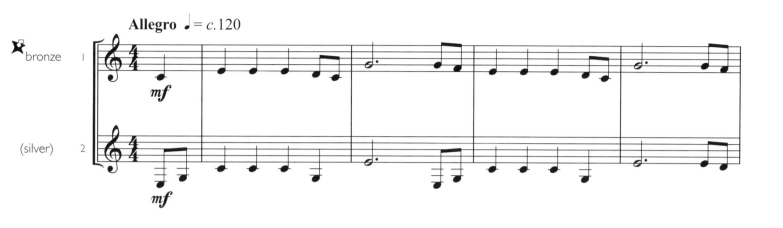

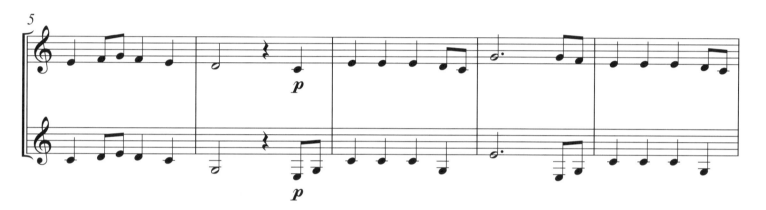

The Reverends Go Rollerblading

Sally Adams

Sunny Intervals

Robert Tucker

Clean Pea Strae

Trad. Scottish arr. Mark Goddard

AB 3027

A Festive Fiesta in Chester

Paul Harris

AB 3027

Ready, or not?

Brian Chapple

Ebony Blues

Alan Haughton

AB 3027

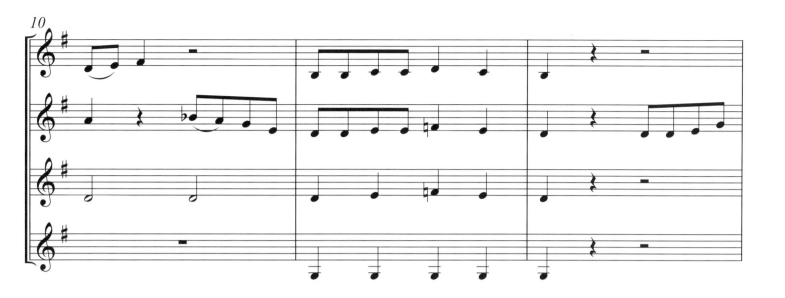

Carousel

Paul Harris

AB 3027

Spicy Noodles

James Rae

The Hammock Swings

Colin Cowles

AB 3027

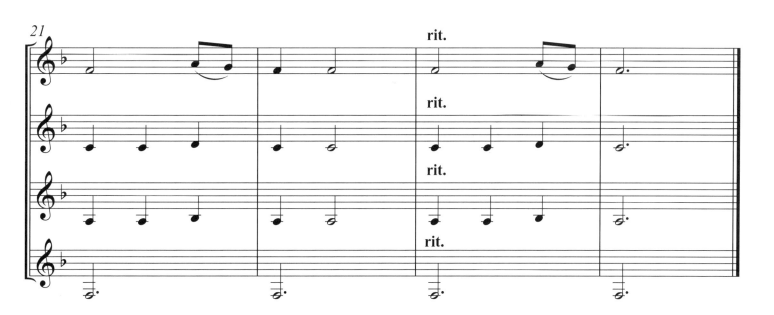